Top Cat had a nap in a cap.

Kit Cat had a nap in a sun hat.

Top Cat had a nap in a big top hat.

Kit Cat had a nap on a mat.
Top Cat had a nap on a rug.

Kit Cat had a nap in a cot.
Top Cat had a nap on a bed.

Pad pad pad! Wag wag wag!
Yap yap yap!

It's a dog! Run, Top Cat!
Run, Kit Cat!

Top Cat and Kit Cat had a nap on top of a van.